The Unwanted Visitor

ELLA FLETCHER

Copyright © 2021 Ella Fletcher

All rights reserved.

ISBN: 978-1-9163441-5-0

DEDICATION

To Max, Harry, Molly, Elsie and Jack.
I love you all, always.

PROLOGUE

Today, I got up, had breakfast, and got ready for school. It was no ordinary school day because I got to wear my own clothes. No boring, uncomfortable uniform for me. And I got to take my favourite things in to share with my mates. Oh yes, today was the best!

Or that is what I would be feeling and thinking if we were breaking up for say Christmas, or Easter, or the summer holidays. Because, well, at least then I would know how long the holidays would last. I would know exactly how many days I would be at home. I would likely be looking forward to going somewhere nice on holiday with my family. I would be expecting to do something like go to the park, catch the latest film at the cinema, or visit a theme park - the list goes on. I would also know when I would be seeing my best friends again.

The problem is, we don't know when we'll go back to school. You see, something major is happening right now. There's this virus, and it's really bad.

Everything is closing in around me.

But it's not just happening to me, it's happening to the whole world.

And I'm scared.

Chapter 1

The first country to fall victim to the virus was China. It's where it all started. Me and my mates heard that, basically, someone had eaten some street food at a market and had become infected! I mean, how could something so simple cause all of this? It's crazy!

We were told the Chinese couldn't celebrate their New Year because they were warning people not to gather in large crowds. And then it got much worse for the country. Soon they wouldn't be able to travel abroad, go to school or work, and then they went into something known as "lockdown".

Hundreds of people were dying every day, and the people who had it were passing it on to other people. It would not stop spreading! I heard my Mom and Dad comment on how bad it must be there for them to take such serious measures.

And then it started spreading to other countries. At first scientists and doctors said it was passed on from anyone who had been in contact with the original people who had been infected or had been to the place where it all started. So, we all thought we would be fine.

Then the scientists and doctors decided that unfortunately, that wasn't the case, and it was rapidly spreading all over the world.

And this is when our parents started to get a little more worried, because now it was getting a bit closer.

Chapter 2

The first time I heard the word "Coronavirus" was on the telly. It was 6 o' clock in the evening and the news was on. "It's time to see what's going on in the world," Mum would say. One day, though, was a bit different - I lost a whole hour of watching my programmes because apparently, "The Prime Minister is going to make an announcement. Shush, be quiet. This is important. This is the biggest thing that's ever happened in our lifetime, this is history."

I rolled my eyes.

Grown-ups don't really give us that much credit, do they? They don't think we understand what is happening around us. But my friends and I do, and we are going to tell you because this is happening to us too.

As the virus started sweeping through countries, one man became a permanent fixture on my telly, our Prime Minister, Boris Johnson, and basically, he is a man that, I swear to God, gets out of bed, brushes his teeth and does absolutely nothing with his hair! I mean, if I even thought about leaving the house to go to school looking like that, my Mum would be dragging me back inside saying, "Come here, you look like nobody owns you!" Or if I did get past her and make it to school, I'd be in trouble for not following the school uniform policy!

Coronavirus is new. It's basically the Mother of all viruses. It affects everyone, but it makes old people, and people who are already sick, really poorly. It won't let me, or my friends go out and mix with each other because us kids are being classed as super-spreaders. And I'll tell you something, if I hear my parents tell me to wash my hands again today, I think I might scream! I know we have to keep them clean, because if we don't, we could pass our germs on.

Talking of germs, this new one, COVID-19, is spreading so quickly that nearly every country in the world has been affected and nothing can stop it apart from the Prime Minister making us self-isolate and stay at home.

Oh, and the worst thing about it is, it's killing people.

Chapter 3

The first thing I remember hearing the Prime Minister say was that we needed to wash our hands a lot, and I mean loads. He also wanted us to sing Happy Birthday twice while we were doing it, which quite frankly made me feel a bit silly, especially when I went to the toilet at school. But we obeyed his rules, well at least us kids did.

The problem was more people became infected in England and so Boris ramped up his rules. We started to hear rumours that school might close, but that wasn't what happened next.

He wanted us to take part in something known as "social-distancing", which, simply put, means he wanted us to avoid shaking and holding hands, and hugging. Instead, he wanted us to bump elbows as a greeting! As if anyone would ever do that!

Then the worst thing happened, for me at least. They started cancelling football matches! Oh man, my favourite thing in the world is football and now I couldn't even watch my favourite team, Wolverhampton Wanderers. Then came the cancellation of all sports, concerts and any other occasions that brought people together. And the rules went on for a while, and as much as I didn't like them, they didn't really affect our lives too badly.

"Unfortunately," the Prime Minister said, "even with these measures that are now in place, the disease is spreading, and the elderly and people with underlying health problems are most at risk."

He started telling us about schools closing at the end of the week. I couldn't believe my luck! The schools would close to all of us, unless our parents had a certain job, or for kids who needed extra carc. Man did I feel sorry for those kids!

Then on the Friday 20th March 2020, the day that I finished school, there was another announcement to say that everywhere would be closing. Leisure centres, cafes, restaurants, gyms, theatres, cinemas, pubs - anywhere you could think of. My Dad said the pubs closing was as bad to him as when I heard that the football matches were off. Poor Dad, I knew exactly what he was going through.

Boris asked people to "stay at home" where possible, and to try not to go out to busy places. The problem is adults aren't always the most sensible people, as much as they try to tell us that they are.

Some people thought that food was going to run out or something like that. I remember hearing the words "panic-buying", which basically meant that some adults got a bit silly and decided to buy as many toilet rolls, bags of pasta and tins of food as possible, until it got so bad the supermarkets made another rule - adults could only buy one of each thing. My Nan said it was like modern day rationing. And it made no sense because The Prime Minister kept saying there was enough to go around if people just took what they needed. I'm not being funny, but us kids are always being told to "Share! Stop being selfish! Don't be spiteful."

The amount of people who were getting the virus kept going up and up and the number of people who were dying from it was also going up. People were not listening. People were still going out, meeting friends, and doing shopping that didn't need to be done.

Boris decided that if someone didn't live in the same house as us, we couldn't see them. This was the first time I'd seen an adult cry. My Mom cried the afternoon we said goodbye to my Nan and Grandad for what could be weeks, maybe longer, even though they only live next door.

The Prime Minister addressed the nation again.

The country was awfully close to "lockdown".

Chapter 4

We were told that we could only leave the house if we really needed to buy important things such as basic food items and medicine. Some businesses could stay open but most closed.

My Mum stopped going to work to look after us and became our teacher. She started taking us out for a walk at seven o' clock in the morning as we were only allowed out of the house once a day to get some exercise. Each morning we would get our coats and shoes on, ready to head out, even though all I wanted to do was chill out in my pj's, watching a film or something. But we would walk, talk and were always back home within the hour. It took me a few days to realise and appreciate that this was the only time we were going to see any sight of anything other than who and what was in our home.

We were still allowed in our gardens and thankfully the weather was nice, so that was good. We had to stay at least two metres away from people. That was okay too.

"These are going to be tough times," my parents said.

For that whole weekend, I listened to my Mum saying, "This won't be a holiday you know. We'll be getting up as normal and you *will* be starting the day at the same time as if you were in school. You have plenty to keep you busy."

No kidding, I thought to myself, remembering how much work had been packed into our bags at school the week before. The teachers must have gone into absolute overdrive. It wouldn't have surprised me if the printer had blown up!

And if that wasn't enough, the school then started sending work through to our User Area on the school website. There's no way my Mum's going to make me get through all of this, she'll definitely lose it before that happens! And anyway, how long do they think we're going to be off for anyway? A year?

Monday 23rd March, the first day of home-schooling, came along way too quickly. Dad gave us a kiss goodbye as he set off for work. He still had to go into work, and I had the feeling he was more than relieved with this situation. I was a little bit jealous that he was leaving the house and we were stuck here. And that made me feel bad because I love him very much.

It had finally hit me, and even then, I couldn't explain the feeling I had. I felt lonely and sad and scared all at the same time.

Chapter 5

To begin with I enjoyed home schooling. It was nice having my Mum teach me things, although, without sounding ungrateful, most of the stuff I already knew. But she seemed pleased with herself for getting through the first day, so I didn't want to burst her bubble.

Then I did actually start learning new things that I wouldn't necessarily have learnt at school. This was a big shock. Mum gave herself a pat on the back, because, as she put it, "At school, teachers have to follow very strict guidelines and jump through so many hoops to get you to where you are now. Here you can learn some of that stuff, but you can also learn about life, and the skills you need to live."

My Mum told me about her job, and I learnt a few skills from that. Then I got to choose what I wanted to learn, and here's a few of the subjects I opted for:

Thanks to my maths lessons, I can now pay for things by adding coins to make different amounts, but it got even more interesting when she showed me how to pay for something using one of her online shopping accounts! Obviously, we had to practise a few times, and she told me not to worry, but we just needed to make sure we got to the door before my Dad in the next few days. Strange.

I chose science as a topic one day and found out that, get this, bones are actually alive. My mind was blown!

For P.E, I learnt how to do backflips on my trampoline, and it was all going brilliantly until my little brother decided to copy me! I've never seen my Mum run so fast up the garden.

I learnt that if you tell your Mum you're tired or better still, have a headache, you get a break instantly which usually gives you at least half an hour to watch some unboxing event happening online!

Apparently, I've also learnt the importance of chores. Not sure of the importance, but what I do know is why Dad never offers to change the sheets – it's a workout in itself! My Mum gets in a bit of a mess when she does them, so I help her with "wafting the duvet", as she calls it. It makes us laugh.

I can navigate a cursor around a laptop using a mouse. My Dad was well impressed! My Mum rolled her eyes when he said to her, "Have you seen what he can do on here!" Her reply told him that yes, she had because she taught me to do it at the start of the week.

The thing is, as much as I loved spending more time at home with my Mum, I found it hard that while she was busy sorting my little brother out, I ended up sitting on my own. He literally cannot do anything on his own. I'm sure I could do more when I was his age! He was getting all the attention and I know I'm older, but I still needed help too. So, at times it was all just a bit boring, just waiting, and it got hard trying to figure some things out for myself when usually my teacher would help me.

The other thing was, at school, in between all the learning, there would be my mates. I miss them so much. I don't get chance to do any of the things I used to do with them. Even though my Mum thinks she's acting really cool and, as she puts it, "down with the kids", she's just not my mate. I love her for trying, I really do, but it's not the same. It's also not the same when she tells me to, "video call your friends if you're missing them". It's not that simple. It's not the same as being with them. It's okay for her. She gets to see my Dad every day, who is the same age as her, so they can talk about things that they have in common. I don't have anyone my age to talk to and this makes me sad.

So as the weeks passed, and the longer I was at home being taught by my Mum, the harder, and the lonelier it got. The lessons became more difficult because my head wasn't in the right place to learn. And I know she found it hard too because she noticed I wasn't enjoying the lessons anymore.

I watched as her bubble began to pop.

Chapter 6

On 26th March 2020, we had almost completed our first, full week in lockdown. Mum was coping surprisingly well. I'd almost finished the first set of worksheets which, when stapled together, looked more like the size of one of the books she's used to reading, and me and my brother hadn't killed each other yet, so we were all feeling like we'd achieved the unachievable.

I overheard my Mum talking to my Dad about something that was going to happen at 8:00pm. Mom told me I was going to get involved, so I did.

At 8 o' clock, everyone in the street stood outside their front door. I heard sounds from the street behind which then seemed to travel to ours. Suddenly, the whole street was clapping, cheering, and banging pots and pans. It was the most wonderful thing I had seen and heard all week! At a time when all I saw was worry on my Mum and Dad's faces, this was pure joy. It seemed to go on and on, nobody wanted to be the first to stop. Nobody wanted this feeling to end. It was magical.

It was called 'Clap for Carers' and it was amazing. You see, the reason we were all in the street (two metres apart, of course) was to show appreciation and thanks to all the NHS staff, and key workers, who were working every day, keeping the country going, whilst doing their very best to try and slow the spread. These people were waking up every morning or every night. They were having a cup of tea and something to eat, getting ready for the day ahead, then saying, "goodbye" to their families, and going to work. Some were working in hospitals; some were working as carers. Some were working in chemists, shops, and supermarkets, providing essential services for us. They were not allowed to "self-isolate" to protect their family. They just had to work and work and work.

It didn't seem enough to just clap for these amazing people, but that's all we could do. Clapping seemed a bit silly, especially as most of them were working at the time. Then we watched the television, saw that everyone all over the country was clapping and all the staff working at the hospitals or on the ambulances saw what we did. It made them cry. It made them say "Thank You" to us. Can you believe that? It made them realise how much we appreciated them. And we do. We always will.

My Mum said, "If anyone ever moans about the NHS again, I'll not be held responsible for my actions!" I've never seen her so angry that she cried before.

The thing I remember most about that night was how everybody came together. Mum said, "We've got this. We can beat this horrible disease." And I really believed her.

Every Thursday night after, I remember people shouting to each other in the street, checking up on neighbours to see if they were okay, asking if anyone needed anything. I saw people caring for each other. Yes, we might have been distancing ourselves from our neighbours, but in that moment, we were closer than we had ever been.

I was proud to have been part of that moment, and I don't think I will ever forget it as long as I live.

Chapter 7

So, there we were, doing all this "social distancing" and I have to say we were all making a good go of it. We had followed all the rules, only going out once a day and staying away from people. Under no circumstances were me and my brother allowed to go into a shop. At first, I thought this was the best news ever! I can't tell you how much I hate doing the food shop with my Mum and Dad. And I have to say, I think they hate taking us too. But by the end of the first few weeks, I'd have just about given anything to walk round a supermarket!

The hardest thing, the thing that hurt the most, the thing that made me the saddest I've ever felt, was not seeing my family. You see, the rule went that you could only have contact with the people you lived with. Which basically meant the last time I saw both sets of my Grandparents was on Mother's Day. The last time I saw cousins, aunties and uncles was before that! Literally the only people I saw were my Mum, my Dad, and my brother. Just imagine that! I mean, I do love them loads but everyone needs other people in their lives.

I missed my Nan's big, squishy hugs, the hugs that made everything seem better again when I was feeling down. I missed playing footy with my Grandad (he's pretty good at it, considering his age!). My Mum tried her hardest to copy Nan's hugs and Grandad's awesome football skills, but she was fighting a losing battle.

Having cousins is a great distraction from trying not to fight with my brother, so it was taking everything I'd got to not punch his lights out.

To try and combat not seeing family in person, we've been video-calling them. It's not great, but it's all we can do to make the best out of a bad situation. My Mum said, "just be thankful you can still see them, some people don't even have that option." She still hadn't caught me doing the eye-rolling thing. I had worked out that all I needed to do was turn away as I was doing it! She kept saying that if not seeing my family for a few weeks helped to slow the spread of the virus, then it's the least we could do. And I guess I can see her point. They were trying to stop the virus spreading from house to house and the quicker they could slow it, the sooner we could all see each other again. I couldn't wait until that day came. Man, it was going to be epic!

It felt strange to think about how we would all feel when it came to an end. I made a promise to pay attention to everyone a little bit more, to listen and love everyone a whole lot more. When I told my Mum this she burst into tears and said, "Well, perhaps it'll all be worth it then."

I think she might be right.

Chapter 8

As I was trying to get used to the idea of not seeing my family, I was also getting used to not seeing my friends. Times were hard.

My Mum still hadn't got the hang of my football cards, and I know adults are always telling us to "never give up", but I tried every way to show her how to do it and she just didn't get it. At all. It was like I was speaking a foreign language! So, yes, I did give up! I also tried to talk her through the rules of my football game on my games console. That was also a major waste of time and believe me I had plenty of it. Time was all I had.

After realising she was failing miserably at being a friend, my Mum decided to do the only thing she could. Again, we turned to technology.

I was allowed to video-call my friends, and apart from the odd bad signal, I finally got to show my mates which swaps I'd sorted in my football cards. We chatted about who we were going to play as, that night on our football game. We talked about how well our parents were doing teaching us and how early we'd sent them to bed! Most of the time, we chatted absolute nonsense to each other because that's what we needed. I acted daft to make them laugh. We fist-bumped our computer screens, laughed as our parents went mental in the background, telling us we better not break anything and asking if we knew how much these things cost.

Then, even though we had only done it a few times, I started to get a bit upset, and quite bored, with video-calling my friends. It made me miss them even more, but it also felt like we didn't have much to say to each other once we had talked about football. So, my Mum came up with an idea. She said, "what about being pen pals?" *Pals with pens?* I thought - that's weird. Pens aren't exactly exciting, are they?

Mum could see my confusion and explained how, when she was a girl, she kept in touch with her best friends with letters. She said she could tell them more in letters than she did on the phone.

So, I wrote each of my friends a letter. I sealed each letter in an envelope, but because they weren't classed as essential mail, Mum said that we would keep them in a safe place. Then when we went back to school, we could hand them out and our friends could read about how much they meant to us. My Mum said this was a great literacy activity too, so we did it as part of one of my English lessons.

I learnt that these times were important. These times made me remember I was still a kid and that I wasn't the only one feeling the way I did. These times reminded me that I still had mates and we were all in the same boat. It made me wonder about what we would do when we eventually got back to school and saw each other. Well for one, our teacher wouldn't be able to keep us quiet, or still, or make us concentrate.

Chapter 9

Things seemed different but still the same. I know, sounds crazy, doesn't it? I thought I was going a little bit mad. My Mum said, "it's cabin fever kid, we're all feeling it. Try not to let it get to you."

It wasn't getting to me, but it was making me feel weird. Let me try and explain.

Take the house. It was still decorated the same. The furniture was still the same, and still in the same place. Everything still looked the same, exactly like it did before. And it took me a while to figure out what the differences actually were.

The drive was different. Both cars were there. All the time. Before, either my Mum was out of the house or my Dad was. There was usually only ever one car on the drive in the daytime. And the house was full, of us. Nobody was out, no visitors were coming in. It was just us.

My Mum and Dad still woke up at the same time, still ate breakfast at the same time. Then dad would take himself to the office he has at home, and there he would hole himself up for the day. He would surface occasionally to make himself a cup of tea. One good thing was he was never late back from work.

Because Mum had a little bit more time than usual, she was spending more time making our meals. She's got loads of recipe books in the kitchen, and some evenings, we ate things that we had never tried before. Most of them were lovely.

My Mum never did anything without us at all. She would set up the day at the table, then sit and go through our work with us. Sometimes it was honestly fun, other times not so much.

My Mum and Dad changed so much. Before all this, when she came back from work, Mum would be busy running us round to different clubs, or picking us up from after school groups, or grandparents houses. But suddenly, she didn't look half as tired. She stopped rushing around to do something or stressing that she'd got "a mountain of ironing to do". She stopped watching documentaries about murders from 50 years ago. To be fair, she was starting to worry my Dad.

The fact is, I was sort of glad this had happened, because I was spending so much time with them both. Mum came on the trampoline with me every day. Dad played football outside with me. His 'nutmeg' was getting almost as good as Grandad's. Mum and Dad were really trying hard for us. Trying to make us laugh. For me, this was the best thing to come out of it all. Yes, they worried about everything that was happening in the world, but it was so good to see them enjoy just not being a grown up.

I saw my parents like I'd never seen them before.

I made my Mum laugh, really laugh. I'd never done that before. My Dad was enjoying our bedtime stories. I know that because he was actually staying awake. And they were finally seeing *me*! They saw how much I was growing up. They saw how hard I work on my schoolwork, and how much I know about the world. And they stopped shielding me from all the problems in it.

Chapter 10

The next big thing that happened was all to do with the Queen. There was an announcement during the news that on Sunday 5th April 2020, she was going to address the nation. To be honest, I had no idea what this meant, so I asked my Mum. To begin with, she shushed me, then realised that I was serious.

"Well, the Queen wants to talk to us, so she's going to be on the telly on Sunday," she said.

"Is that it?" I replied, thinking the announcement was a bit over the top just to let us know the Queen was going to talk to us.

"Son, this will be an especially important moment," my Mum replied, "You see, the Queen doesn't usually address the nation very often."

"She's on every Christmas Day," I said.

"Yes, true, but that's tradition. Let me ask you this, do you ever see her giving a message on the television apart from Christmas Day?"

I thought hard, and I couldn't think of any other time when I had seen her on the TV.

"No," I replied after a while.

"Well," she said, "This is huge, and another part of our history. You see, the Queen has only addressed the nation on a few occasions, so it's quite a big deal. The first time she did it was when she was fourteen years old. She sat with her sister, Princess Margaret, and addressed all the children who were being evacuated during the second world war. She also addressed the nation when the Gulf War happened, when Princess Diana died, when her Mum, the Queen Mother died, and for her Diamond Jubilee. If you think how long the queen has been on the throne for, that's not many times is it?"

And so, at 8 o' clock in the evening, Sunday 5th April she appeared on our telly. She praised the NHS staff, and all key workers, for everything they were doing. She thanked us for staying at home and following the guidelines the Government was giving us. She said she understood how hard people were finding it all, especially the fact that we were not allowed to see family and friends through it all. And then she finished by saying, "We will be with our friends again. We will be with our families again. We will meet again."

The house fell silent for a few minutes after the programme finished. I looked at my Mum and Dad. They were still, just staring into space, then Mum started to cry a bit. I didn't say anything, I just watched them. I didn't need to ask them how serious it all was because I could see it in their faces. So, I did the same – sat still and stared at the telly. The Queen's words meant so much to Mum and Dad in that moment. And suddenly, my Mum seemed to come to life again.

"Well, Liz you did it again," she said.

"What do you mean?" I asked.

"Well, Max, that Lady is in her nineties now. She has served the country for sixty-eight years! Most people retire in their sixties. She's always had to follow very strict, royal rules that are out of date for these times, but she's never moaned, and she's never been in any trouble. I've watched her since I was little. Nanny and Grandad weren't even born when she became Queen, so they've watched her all their lives too! That's two generations of our family that have had her as their Queen. Nobody has served longer than her. And yet again she comes on the television, she talks, and we listen. The country listens. That, my boy, is one heck of a gift."

My Mum's words, and the Queen's, made me stop and think. Think of how much I'm looking forward to being with my family again, and to see my friends again, and I'm excited for the world to meet again.

Chapter 11

After the Queen's speech, the house seemed quite peaceful and content. The day after the speech I heard it again, quite a few times, as different channels showed clips of it. Mum and Dad seemed to have fallen into a calm pattern of working from home and teaching my brother and I as best as they could. Mum was constantly sending evidence of us doing our work to school and we were getting more and more work sent back. I'm not going to lie, it just never seemed to end.

And then the feeling in the house changed again, as it was reported that the

Prime Minister had caught the virus. People were worried again. After getting used to a certain way of life, adapting to it, and coping quite well, we came back down to earth with a bump. It's really strange because I never thought the Prime Minister could catch it! I mean the number of times I had seen him on TV reminding people how to behave and how to live, and then he gets it!

So, the panic set in again, and again, all I seemed to hear was what not to do, how to live safely and whatever we do, we had to stay at home if possible. I don't know about anyone else, but it seemed that as soon as we started to cope with everything, something else always came along to upset things.

We didn't see the Prime Minister for nearly two weeks. He was taken to hospital where he spent time on the Intensive Care Unit. I asked Dad what that meant.

"Only very, very poorly people spend time on these wards," he said, then reminded me just how serious the situation was.

I made sure I always washed my hands after that.

Around this time, I heard Mum say, "Right, I can't watch the news all day now! It's just too depressing!" So, the only time we heard about it was when we were having breakfast, and when it was on in the evening.

Her mood became more positive again, and she pushed worry back around the corner, where she said it belonged.

Chapter 12

A phrase I heard all through lockdown was, "when this is all over...".

I enjoyed listening to what I nicknamed, *The Firsts*. The first person someone wanted to hug, the first thing someone wanted to buy, the first place someone wanted to visit, the first holiday people were going to book. And the first pub my Mum and Dad wanted to visit. One night, as I lay in bed, I thought about my *firsts*. It was hard. Not because I didn't know what I wanted them to be (that I had known for ages), it was the fact that we didn't know when we would have our *firsts*.

I wanted things that didn't mean so much, like going to the toy shop and buying a console game I had saved for. I wanted to go to the local park where there is a proper football pitch and goals. I wanted to see and play with someone other than my brother. I wanted to go back to my after-school clubs where I spent time with my mates. They were the things that didn't hurt too much to think about.

And then I got to the people and places that meant the most to me. I missed seeing my grandparents. I missed them so much that sometimes it made my entire body ache. I'm very close to all of my cousins, so not seeing them was really hard, and I could not wait until I saw them again. My youngest cousin has actually started walking. That's how much I have missed.

I couldn't wait to go back to school to be with all my mates. I missed the fun we had, the games we played and the challenges we used to set each other. I wasn't so crazy about the lesson side of it, but neither were my mates, so I'm sure we would struggle through together.

I couldn't wait to see my Mum give her Mum and Dad hugs, and my Dad hug his parents. I can't imagine what it would be like to not be able to give my Mum and Dad hugs or spend time with them. The one thing I loved about lockdown was having them around so much. We found different ways to enjoy our time, and Mum said we saved lots of money because we weren't going out.

When all of this is over, we would be together again. And that was my last thought as I fell asleep.

Chapter 13

The days seemed to pass quite quickly. Apart from the weekends. My Mum said she found the weekends harder to deal with, because that's when we'd usually see the family.

We tried to focus on the little things. The weekly 'Clap for Carers' was something we looked forward to. Strange really; if we weren't in lockdown there's no way I would have gone outside at 8 o'clock on a Thursday night with my parents to clap for something. I'd either be in bed or playing on my computer game. But, as it was, getting to these points generally meant we were almost finished with another week of lockdown. Which meant one thing – we were one week closer to things getting back to normal. And that could only be a good thing.

So, there we were, passing the days with attempted schoolwork, Mum's new hobby of gardening, which she made everyone do, and baking cakes to keep my brother quiet.

We were making a fine job of it, I have to say, but then the government was going to announce if the country needed to stay in lockdown for another three weeks! I heard Mum tell Dad in the kitchen that morning, "I'm dreading the outcome later. Another three weeks of not going anywhere. Not seeing family and trying to keep everything positive for the boys. It's getting so hard."

Then the daily briefings started. People throughout the country would be holding their breath. Some dared to hope, while others knew exactly what was coming. Lockdown was to continue and would be assessed in another three weeks, and even though we knew this could happen, it was still hard to hear.

We all felt a bit deflated to be honest. Mum is doing a good job, but she's getting worried that three or four lessons a day isn't really enough to prepare me for next year. And she said, "You're not going to know what's hit you when you do go back."

I thought about another three weeks and what it meant for me: At least three more weeks of not seeing my friends. Three weeks of not seeing family. Three weeks of home learning.

I felt a bit down. Mum noticed this and all she said was, "Another three weeks of staying safe, we can do this." She kissed me on the top of the head and said, "We'll get there, love, I promise."

Chapter 14

The week after the government announced another three weeks of lockdown, I celebrated my birthday.

I should have been having my dream party. It was going to be held at The Molineux, the home of my favourite football team, the Wolves. I was really looking forward to it. Friends, football, food and fun. What more could I possibly ask for? My party was due to be held the Sunday before my birthday, which meant I would be celebrating over a few days.

And then, due to lockdown, my dream party was cancelled. I was really sad, but on the other hand, I was looking forward to spending my birthday at home, all day. I wouldn't have to rush to open my presents in the morning, and then wait all day until I could get back and play with them.

So, I got to open all my presents, in my own time. I got loads of football kits, and I made it my goal to wear each and every one of them before the day was out. I played every one of my new computer games. And as an extra bonus, no home-schooling!

I missed not having all my family over for a birthday tea, and lots of cake. I missed them all not being in the house, watching me open the gifts they had bought me. I did get to see them for a little bit. They all came round, and they stood at the end of our drive, but their visits were spaced out through the day, and what was really weird was that they couldn't give me my presents, they had to put them on the floor, then move away, so that I could pick them up. Mum got a bit upset, and then my

Nan got upset because Mum and my Aunty were upset. It really was very strange.

There were some parts to my lockdown birthday that were loads better. I loved that I didn't have to go to school for that one day. But birthdays are for sharing, aren't they? And I felt like I couldn't really share it enough with the people I love the most, and the friends I like the most. Friends who I have more in common with than my Mum and Dad. I didn't get the hugs I would've had, the kind which would've probably made me a bit embarrassed, but deep down meant the most to me.

I will never forget having a birthday during lockdown for many reasons, but the main reason is how much Mum and Dad tried to make the absolute best time for me even though it was hard for them.

I'll never let them know that I will probably remember it as the loneliest birthday I've ever had.

Chapter 15

May Day had been changed for this year only. And for once it had nothing to do with the flipping Coronavirus!

Usually, May Day is the first Monday of May. We wouldn't have been in school because it is a Bank Holiday. But this year it had been changed to a Friday. When I asked mom why, she told me a little about the Second World War. How long it lasted and how, when Germany surrendered, there were street parties all over the country. That day became known as VE Day, which meant Victory in Europe. This year marks 75 years since the end of the Second World War.

Now, because we were all in lockdown the government advised everyone to have a party on their drive (keeping 2 metres apart, obviously). We had our street party, with our sandwiches and scones. We listened to music from the 40's, and we relaxed in the sunshine.

Mum and Dad really wanted us to have an idea what it may have been like for someone of my age during the Second World War. So, naturally, Mum made me do some schoolwork about it. I found out an awful lot about how children lived in the cities, and the danger they faced, and terrible things they saw. I learnt about how some children were sent away to live in the country with complete strangers, and how some children never saw their families or moved back home again. Then Mum asked me to talk to my friends about it, using messaging, to find out how our lives are different now, in the most dangerous time we've lived in. So, we did a little comparison study and here are the results:

- **Lockdown Compared to Evacuation:** My friends and I decided that even though this is the hardest thing we've lived through so far in our life at least we're at home with our parents.
- **Lockdown Compared to The Blitz:** The Blitz was when the Germans began bombing the UK. People and children had to use Air raid shelters when the bombings took place. When they heard the warning sirens, they had to go underground and wait until it was safe to come out. The sights they faced when they came out of the shelters would not have been pleasant. During lockdown we've had to stay in our warm homes with all of our favourite

things to keep us entertained and safe.

- **Lockdown Compared to War:** There are some similarities, we all supposed. Thousands of people died throughout the Coronavirus outbreak. Many were 'frontline' workers, trying to save the lives of the many people who caught the virus.

After I'd chatted to my friends about it, Mom said to me, "Now tell me when you would prefer to live, then or now?"

Instantly I said, "Now, of course!"

"Precisely," she said, "So, when you're feeling sad that you can't see your friends, imagine what those children felt all those years ago when their parents put them on a train, and waved goodbye to them until, hopefully, the war was over, not knowing at all when that would be."

I just looked at her.

"Then imagine," she went on, "hearing the siren to tell you to find cover while the bombs were being dropped, and then finally coming out of the shelters to find you hadn't got a home anymore."

I looked around at the living room.

"And imagine that you never got to see your friends anymore because a bomb had landed on their shelter," she finished with.

My mouth fell open and my Dad said, "Oh that's a bit much, don't you think, love?"

During that conversation with Mum, I soon realised that as hard as the whole situation we were in felt, I knew there would be an end to it. I realised that the people I love, and the friends that I missed so much, were still there, being kept safe by their families. I have so much to be thankful for.

Chapter 16

On the Sunday before the eighth week of lockdown, we were informed that Boris Johnson was going to address the nation. Well, I'd heard this term a few times now, so I no longer had to ask what it meant. What I did ask Mum and Dad was, "Why?"

Dad was quick to respond, "Well, the Prime Minister is going to tell us what the next stage of lockdown will look like, and how we will have to live and adapt to it. It's important, and it gives us hope that soon, we'll be able to live as normally as possible again. This is positive."

Dad told me to write down how I felt after the speech.

I wrote that I felt a bit confused and worried, and that I was hoping that we'd be able to see the people we loved outside of our house. We still couldn't see them, but we could take longer exercise times.

WHAT? I'm not being funny, an hour was all good with me, but the moment my Mum got wind of it, believe me, I knew it would never be enough!

People could return to work, only if it was safe to do so. So, my Dad had to swap the home office for his work office. I got a bit worried, and nervous. Mum knew this and talked me through the changes Dad would be making at work to stay as safe as possible. She said it would be strange at first, but we would soon get used to it, just like we had got used to everything else.

We were told we could see one other person outside of our home, as long as it was not in our home. Well, I didn't know why they had to say this because most people were already doing it! We stood on Nan and Grandad's drive talking to them. I got quite angry and upset. It's even harder when you know you can see them but can't hug them.

The Prime Minister said more details would be given the following day to help us, and once we had waded through them, things seemed a bit more promising.

One day I met Grandad at the front of the house, and we went to play football on a field. Mum reminded me that I was not allowed to hug him, and I needed to stay two metres apart.

Grandad and I both agreed this had been the best afternoon since lockdown started, especially when I perfectly 'nutmegged' him!

Chapter 17

One day I said to Mum, "I can't wait to go back to normal."

Mum said something really strange, or at least it was strange until she explained it to me in the way only parents can.

"Oh, we'll never go back to normal, kid. We'll go forward, to a new normal, and we'll be just fine with that."

I thought she'd finally lost the plot and told her that that didn't make any sense!

"Just think about all of the things you've learnt during lockdown?"

"Don't you roll your eyes at me," she said, "you're doing that an awful lot now and it needs to stop."

I kept quiet and looked at the floor.

"If we went back to normal, what would you miss?" she asked.

I shrugged my shoulders. Something else she's not a fan of.

She then reminded me of the times we'd sat outside listening to the birds, so clear and loud that we heard nothing else. She reminded me of the things we'd learned in the garden, and all the evenings we'd looked at the stars, and the days where there wasn't a cloud in the sky. She reminded me of the hours we'd spent laughing and crying, and how we'd learnt to appreciate what we already had.

Mum didn't want to go back to normal, and to be honest, thinking about it, I don't think I did either.

"We must remember the good things that have happened during the lockdown and take them forward," she said, "It'll be a different *normal*, where we will still have to remember to enjoy life at a distance, and take time to care for, and enjoy, nature. And now, more than ever, we will not be rushing through life. Instead, we will appreciate the moment we are living in."

I got it then.

Just as I was appreciating that moment a letter came from school.

It announced that my school planned to reopen for a few year-groups.

I was in one of them.

On 8th June 2020, I was going back to school. I was going to see my teacher and my friends.

I took a deep breath, smiled, and let the good news wash over me, and then sorted my football card swaps, ready for the big day.

Chapter 18

I had a million butterflies in my tummy. I was so excited about going back to school, but a little bit nervous too. I was worried I wouldn't sleep, but Mum said, "Don't you worry about that, kid. You'll sleep, and I'm sure you'll have the best dreams."

Earlier on, I'd watched her, and helped a bit, tidy the dining room table of all the home-schooling clutter. She unplugged the laptop and computer monitor. She moved pen-pots, reams of paper, scissors, and glue. Then she came to my exercise books. She picked them up, stroked the covers and just kept looking at them. She sighed as she opened them, looking over all the work we had miraculously managed to cover during lockdown.

"Are you okay, Mum?" I asked her, "You seem a bit sad."

"I'm not sad, love," she replied.

I'm not being funny, but she so was. I know her well enough to know when she's upset.

"Really?"

"No. I'm just thinking of all the time we've put into these books, the arguments we've had, the fun, the moaning, the worrying. All of those memories are stored in these pages now, and I'll remember them always," she sighed.

"These books of yours," she went on, "aren't just about those English lessons you hated, or the maths worksheets you loved doing. They're not just about the topic work you kept forgetting, and the art we had a go at. These books show us something we did together, just you and me. We achieved this together. We smashed it. Most of the time. We may have been driven to the brink of hysteria, and back again, but we never gave up!"

I didn't roll my eyes. I didn't moan. I nodded. And smiled.

"So, no, I'm not sad," she smiled at me, "I'm proud of you, and I'm proud of myself too. I'm proud of us. And I hope that when you go back to school tomorrow, the work won't seem too hard, and the days won't be too tiring, because even though you weren't at school, we reminded ourselves that schoolwork is so very important."

And with that, Mum said our home schooling was, "over and out!"

Chapter 19

I couldn't believe it. In just a couple of hours, I would be walking to school with my Mum. My head felt giddy and the butterflies from the night before were still fluttering away.

Apparently, we weren't allowed hot dinners at school. We needed to take packed lunches. Mum asked me what I wanted on my sandwiches. She smiled when I answered, telling her everything I wanted, and it reminded me of how things used to be.

When I'd eaten my breakfast, Mum sent me upstairs for a shower. This was new. She said she wanted me, "as clean as a whistle" and that I would now be having a shower every morning, because it would be one less thing for the teachers to worry about, and because my hair was so long that when I got up in the morning, it looked like nobody owned me.

I got changed into my school uniform and it felt weird. Weird but kind of good. I hadn't worn a shirt, or anything else with buttons on for that matter, all the way through lockdown.

Mum went through all the new school rules with me. It was a lot to take in, to be honest, but I knew I would have to stick to them all. And just before we left the house, she made me stand against a wall, so she could take a photo of me. She told me she had been longing for this day.

We walked to school and when we got there, I was greeted by a teacher, who ticked my name off a list. Then, we walked to my classroom, and Mrs Jones smiled at me, and all my butterflies disappeared.

She told me all about washing my hands before going into class, which I did, and I did it every time afterwards.

I met my bubble of friends. There were six of us. Three boys and three girls. We sat on different tables which were spaced out. The great thing was, I wasn't nervous, because school had already sent my Mum photos of my classroom, which I had looked at too, so I knew what to expect.

We all worked hard and had lots of fun. To be honest, the kids in my group weren't my closest friends but it didn't matter one little bit. We all just wanted to be at school with kids of the same age, no matter who they were. We all learnt things about each other that we didn't know before.

My bubble meant the world to me. I don't think I'll ever forget the kids that were in it. We'll always remember that we were one of the first groups that could go back to school after lockdown. It's something very special, and something we will have in common forever.

Chapter 20

The day after I returned to school, my brother started back. He was put in a key worker group because my Mum needed to go back to work. She's a teaching assistant in a school and had been to work for one day each week since lockdown began, but now she needed to go back more regularly, so my brother needed to go back to school. Because he wasn't in any of the ages that were asked to return in bubbles, he joined a group where there were kids of all ages. These kids all had parents who could not stay at home, parents who had to go to work to help others.

Mum was more worried about my brother going back than me. She said it was because he was younger and hadn't ever done a full day at school, which he was going to find hard. I think she was worried for the teachers too because to be honest, when my brother has not had his sleep, he's a right monster!

But it was lovely walking to school together. He was so excited to finally be taking a lunch box! It doesn't sound like much, but it was a huge deal to him.

We found out that his nursery teacher would be in the key worker group. Mum was so relieved and told Dad, "If anyone can calm him down, she can!"

And so, our schooling became the "new normal". Our life was more interesting on account of the people and kids we got to see. Weeks were broken up into weekdays and weekends again. Every day was different to the one before. I never felt too bored.

School was the place for learning, home the place for chilling. And I don't think I've ever been so tired. Seriously. Mum said it was because I was using my brain more.

Chapter 21

The summer holiday was brilliant. We didn't go on as many days out as we usually do in the six weeks, but it didn't matter too much because we were still going to Goathland in North Yorkshire. We didn't know if we would still be able to go, but we did, and it was amazing. It was the first time in ages that all the family got together in one house and me, my brother and my cousin Molly were so happy. And when we found out we could use the pool in the garden of the cottage, we were really excited. The first few times we used it, it was freezing cold, but it didn't matter. We got used to it after a while and we had so much fun jumping in and splashing about.

We did lots of walking on the moors which was brilliant. It was just nice to be somewhere that wasn't near to us. It felt like proper fresh air. One evening, we all went up on the hill behind the cottage to watch the sun go down and the moon come out. It was so cold and at one point, I was a bit annoyed that the adults were dragging us out of the warm, cosy cottage, but I'm glad we did it because the view was amazing.

We still got to visit our favourite shops, and go to the pub for dinner, as long as the adults wore their masks and used hand gel, but that was the same as anywhere and it didn't bother my family at all.

The holiday was so good. It was the most fun I'd had in ages, but it couldn't last forever. Nothing that's that much fun does.

The new school year started without too much confusion, for me, at least. The same could not be said for my parents. The times I heard Mum talking to herself, reminding herself as much as us of what days P.E was on, what we needed to take to school, what we couldn't take to school, the rules and times of pick-ups and drop offs, of forms that had to be filled out and handed in. The list could go on forever.

In September I was no longer in a bubble of six. My bubble was now my whole year group. Amazing! Unfortunately, I couldn't take cards to swap, but the football games at lunch times were epic because there was now enough in our class to make a decent team!

My brother went to his year group too. It felt very different because it was such a normal thing to do, and we hadn't been used to anything normal for a long time.

Outside of school my football started up again, I have never been so excited. Swimming lessons started again too, and we actually managed to go on holiday! Things weren't exactly the same as they were before lockdown, but they were still pretty amazing. They were so special because we weren't sure if we would be able to do any of them again this year.

As life started to get back to how it once was, problems began to show again. Cases began to rise again, and another lockdown happened. This one was a little different. Only non-essential shops, pubs, restaurants, and leisure closed down again. This time for four weeks. Which meant I carried on going to school, but my football stopped again, and so did my swimming. Mum said, "It's literally all work and no play." But this was all to try and make sure we could have a Christmas spent with some family.

And that's all that mattered to me.

So, we followed the rules. Again.

THE ART

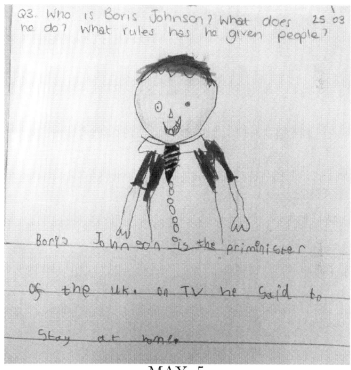

Q3. Who is Boris Johnson? What does 25 03 he do? What rules has he given people?

Boris Johnson is the priminister of the uk. on TV he said to Stay at home.

MAX, 5

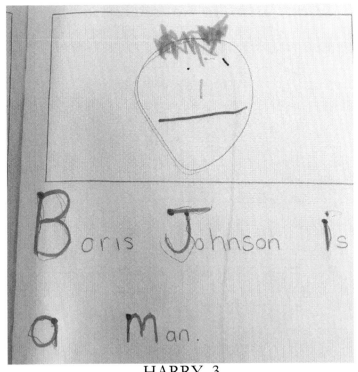

HARRY, 3

MOLLY, 10

I think Boris Johnson is a good PM because he is trying his best to keep us safe through this epic pandemic, but there are so many people that arn't listening to his advice.

By
Amelia
Foster

AMELIA, 10

Boris is the Prime Minister.
You can jog once a day. Keep
2 metres apart. You cant
meet friends or go to school.

THEO, 6

Boris Johnson is the prime minister. He said my dad can not go to work but my mom still has to go

CRUZ, 6

he looks like donald trump with diffrent hair. He wunts us to stay in owr house

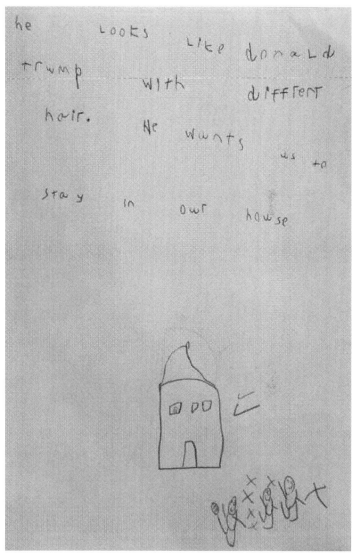

NOAH, 5

Boris Johnson is the prime minister of England. He has set some rules for this occasion (Covid-19 or coronavirus). His rules are to: Stay inside, don't go in public places, try to keep the recommended 2 metres away from eachother, don't have visitors in your house, schools have shut (but the Nurses or doctors children have to go to school). The only shops that are open are Supermarkets for food.

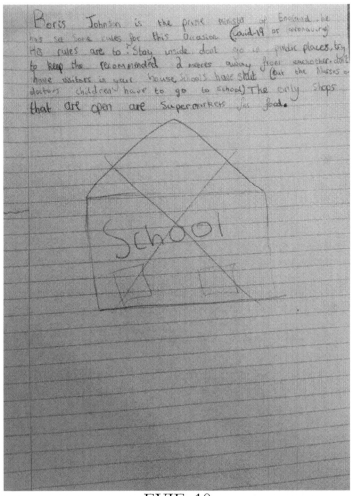

EVIE, 10

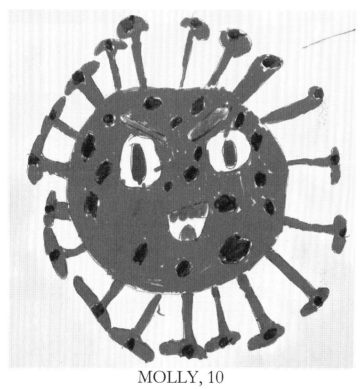

MOLLY, 10

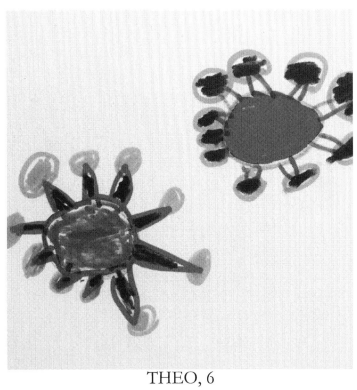

THEO, 6

SCARLETT, 6

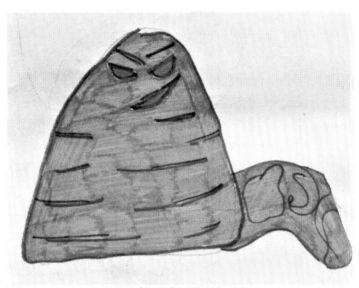

ELSIE SMITH, 10

JENSON, 4

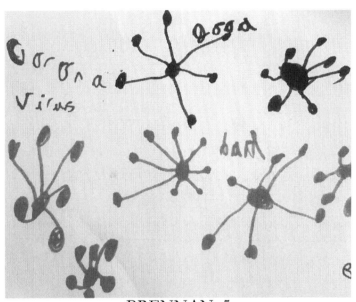

BRENNAN, 5

CERYS, 4

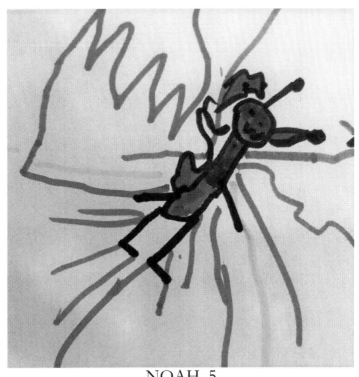

NOAH, 5

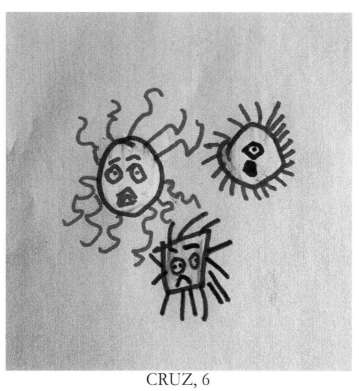

CRUZ, 6

ZELIKA, 10

AMELIA, 10

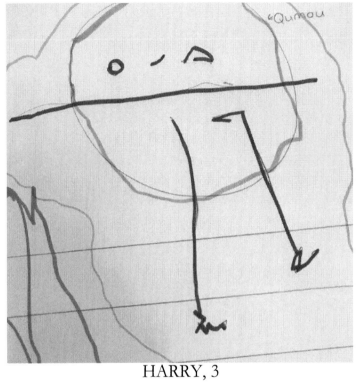

HARRY, 3

ELSIE WEBBER, 6

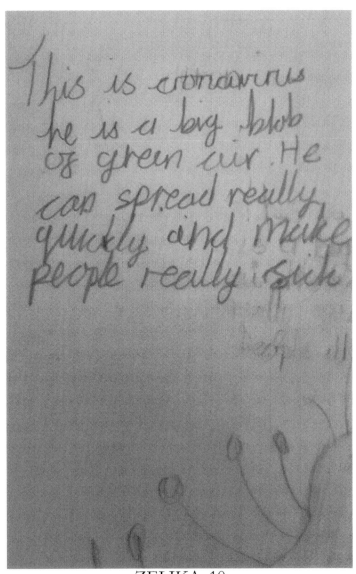

This is coronavirus he is a big blob of green air. He can spread really quickly and make people really sick.

ZELIKA, 10

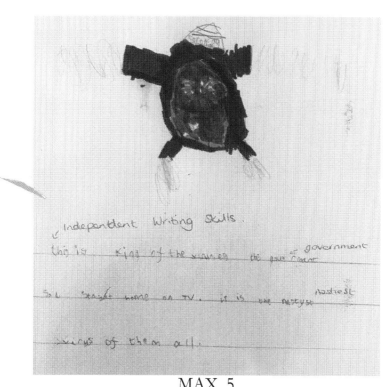

Independent Writing Skills.

This is kind of the scaries the government

See scary home on TV. it is the nastiest
thing of them all.

MAX, 5

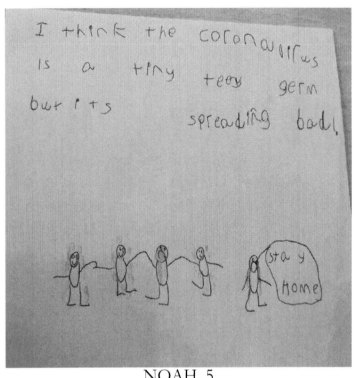

I think the coronavirus
is a tiny teey germ
but its spreading bad!

stay
Home

NOAH, 5

It is like a type of germ.
It will affect old people
and people poorly.
People Must stay in.

SCARLETT, 6

The coronavirus is a nasty
bug that spreads across the
planet and kills people.
It makes me sad.

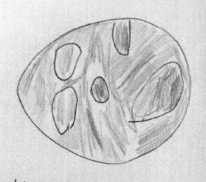

Keep Safe

THEO, 6

AMELIA, 10

I think, the coronavirus is a virus that kills old people because of the batteria germs and victims of animals. It can kill old people or can kill people with problems with their body. This virus is a new virus that doesn't allow us to go outside in public places, (but only alad in our own backyards)

Be safe

EVIE, 10

AMELIE, 8

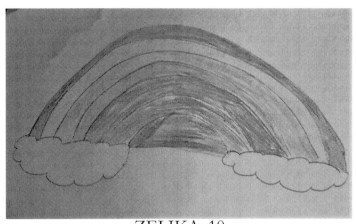

ZELIKA, 10

ELSIE SMITH, 10

MOLLY, 10

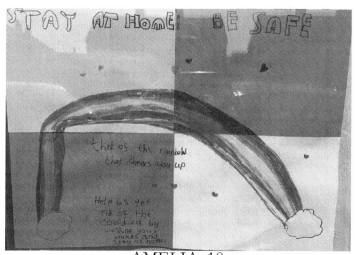

AMELIA, 10

AMELIE, 8

I don't like learning at home, because my younger sisters (twins toddle) get all the attention and get help but theirs me just sitting down, not knowing what to do at all and then I just don't get any help and don't get any attention at all.

EVIE, 10

I like doing my work at home because my mom is my teacher and it is fun but I miss my friends and my teacher

CRUZ, 6

I think the coronavirus
is a nasty bug that
jumps on your hands and
makes people poorly and
makes people sad.

CRUZ, 6

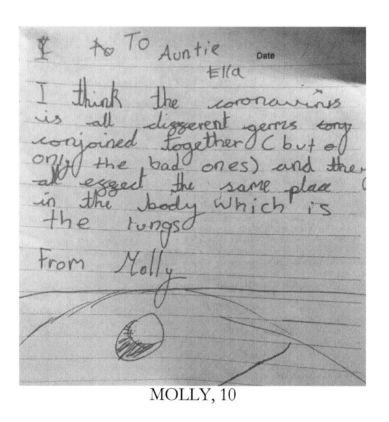

to TO Auntie   Date
Ella

I think the coronavirus
is all different germs
conjoined together (but
only the bad ones) and the
all effect the same place
in the body which is
the lungs

From Molly

MOLLY, 10

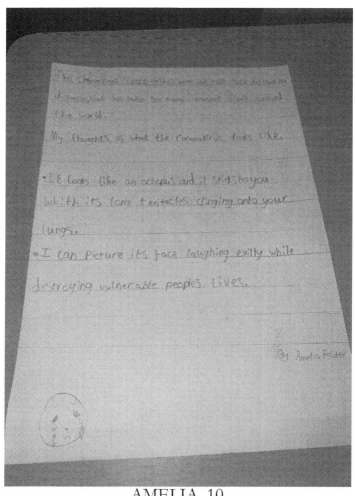

The coronavirus scares me that we will soon be defeated by disease, that has taken too many innocent lives around the world.

My thoughts of what the coronavirus looks like.

• It looks like an octopus and it sticks to you with its long tentacles clinging onto your lungs.

• I can picture its face laughing evilly while destroying vulnerable peoples lives.

By Amelia Foster

AMELIA, 10

I feel sad that I don't see my friends. I miss them.

cruz Theo max

Noah

THEO, 6

I feel angry because of the corona. I miss my nan, granded, aunties, uncles, grannar, grantas, my best friends. I miss playing with them and I don't know when I will see them. I just want to have a hug. I love my family soooo much. I really miss my friends. I wanna see the sea.

AMELIE, 8

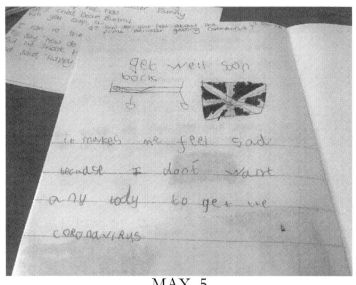

MAX, 5

Boris Johson's Rules

ONLY LEAVE HOME TO:
* Shop for basic necessities - infrequently.
* ONE form of exercise a day.
* Medical need or to provide care or to help a vulnerable person.
* Travelling to and from work, where this is absolutely necessary.

BANNED
* Meeting friends.
* Meeting relatives you don't live with.
* All weddings, baptisms and ceremonies except funerals.
* Gathering bigger than two people.

CLOSED
* All shops selling non-essential goods.
* All libraries, playgrounds, outdoor gyms and places of worship.

STILL OPEN:
* Parks, but they will be patrolled.

POLICE POWERS To:
* Disperse gatherings.
* Fine rule-breakers.

AMELIA, 10

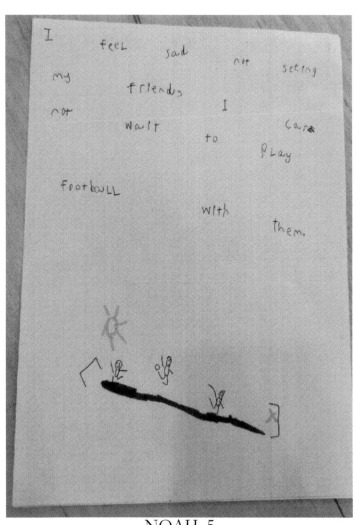

I feel sad not seeing my friends not I want to care play feotbaLL with them.

NOAH, 5

I think my mom and dad are still the same.

NOAH, 5

Q2 What is the Coronavirus and What does it do?

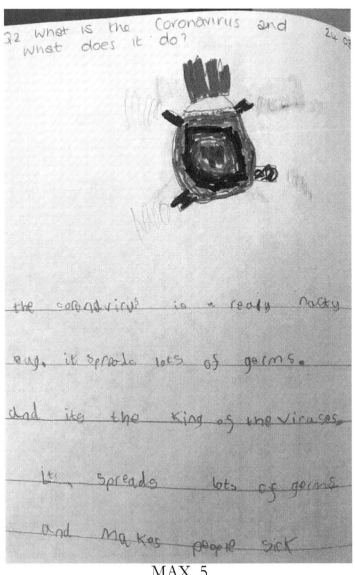

the coronavirus is a realy nasty bug. it spreads lots of germs. and its the King of the viruses, it spreads lots of germs and makes people sick

MAX, 5

Lerning at home feels different Because I don't get to see my friends and I miss my teachers.

NØ because I am doing work from School exept P.E because I do that on youtube at P.E With Joe

AMELIA, 10

It makes me sad to not
see my Family. I miss
them. I sent my man
a card that I made to
cheer her up.

CRUZ, 6

A NOTE FROM THE AUTHOR

Amongst the very first pages of this book, before all the good stuff starts, you'll find a title page. On that title page, it states that I, Ella Fletcher, am the author. But there's something I would like to point out - I'm not really the author at all. There are many authors of this book and I'm going to name them all shortly.

I had the idea for The Unwanted Visitor, as I was about to embark on home-schooling my boys, who were five and three at the time. I wanted to know what was going through their wonderful little heads. At times, as parents, I think we fail to realise just how much our children are taking in and understanding, so it was a way for me to keep tabs on how they were feeling amidst all the chaos and confusion.

Then I spoke to a few, fellow parents of my boy's friends, and asked if they wanted to take part, which they all, amazingly, did. I then asked my niece to join in, who in turn invited some of her closest friends to take part. This was great because then we had opinions and perspectives of older children. It was perfect! In a time where we were socially deteriorating, it encouraged them all to talk more, and to listen.

The points of view of the young people involved have demonstrated how grown up they all are, and that's why I don't think I can call them kids, not anymore. Children shouldn't have a care or worry in the world. The day this pandemic started my boys were no longer *kids*. I saw worry and fear when I should have seen fun and laughter. I saw them cope with grief as if they had lost a member of the family. I saw them question things that no kid should ever have to question. My boys lost some of the pure innocence that every child has an abundance of.

But from doing this book I have realised not what they have learnt from us, but what we can learn from them – the resilience they've shown, the drive to just get on with things. I admire and commend them for how they have constantly adapted to every twist and turn in the road, and for how they never give up.

So, my thanks (not just for this book, but for the lessons I have learnt through all of this) go to the following young people who answered all the questions I threw at them (and, of course, huge thanks to the parents who said yes to taking part): Max and Harry Fletcher, Molly Onions, Noah Fisher, Scarlett and Jenson Moreton, Theo Yeomans, Cruz Williams, Evie, Amelie and Elsie Webber, Cerys and Brennan McCormack, Zelika Brown, Elsie Smith, and Amelia Foster.

These young people have totally inspired me, and I hope they realise that they are the voices of a generation. They are the kids who *owned* lockdown 2020/2021.

As a teaching assistant, I know how much hard work has gone into home schooling throughout lockdown, but I still need to mention our amazing teachers and TA's, who have not only produced and provided excellent content throughout lockdown but have been a constant support to our children (and us, their parents).

I offer my sincere gratitude to my sister, Lucy Onions, and the wonderful, James Josiah, of Bright Dream for their editing, formatting, and proofreading skills. The Unwanted Visitor wouldn't be here, in your hands, if it wasn't for their expertise.

I also want to thank all my family for their encouragement and support in everything I do. My love to you all.

THE KIDS

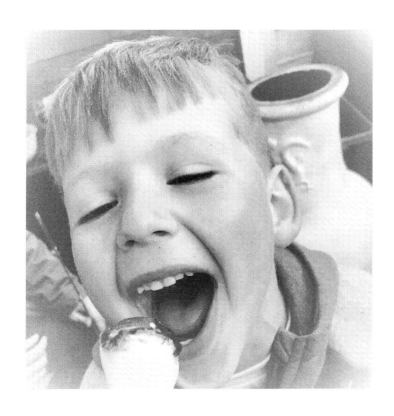

ME, MAX

MY BROTHER, HARRY

MY COUSIN, MOLLY

ME AND HARRY WITH OUR COUSINS,
ELSIE AND JACK CHAPMAN

ME AND HARRY WITH MY FRIENDS,
THEO AND NOAH

ZELIKA

CRUZ

AMELIA

AMELIE

ELSIE SMITH

ELSIE WEBBER

SCARLETT AND JENSON

EVIE

CERYS AND BRENNAN

ABOUT THE AUTHOR

Ella lives in Willenhall, West Midlands with her husband, Paul and her two boys, Max and Harry, and their retired greyhound, Meggy-Doo.

Ella is a full-time, Special Educational Needs Teaching Assistant at Wightwick Hall School, and loves her job immensely. She's a dab hand when it comes to arts and crafts, and spends time with her boys, making lots of lovely, homemade goodies. She loves to read, tell, and write stories. Some of the stories she writes make their way into books just like this. Others are secret, just for her and her family… for now.

You can find out more about Ella here:
https://www.facebook.com/EFletch/

Printed in Great Britain
by Amazon

62965825R00097